Three-Minute Bible Stories with Cut and Paste Projects

by Kenneth Munn

illustrated by Janet Armbrust

Cover by Dan Grossmann

Copyright © 1994

Shining Star Publications

ISBN No. 0-86653-776-7

Standardized Subject Code TA ac

Printing No. 9876

Shining Star
A Division of Frank Schaffer Publications, Inc.
23740 Hawthorne Boulevard, Torrance, CA 90505-5927

Unless otherwise indicated, the New International Version of the Bible was used in preparing the activities in this book.

INTRODUCTION

Three-Minute Bible Stories with Cut and Paste Projects was especially designed for busy teachers. Each story can be presented in two to three minutes. Stories about Noah, Abraham, Rebekah, Joseph, Moses, Samson, Eli, David, Elijah, Jonah, and Jesus are included. Each cut-and-paste craft has a reproducible pattern. The only supplies needed to complete most of the Bible-based projects are crayons, scissors, and glue. After children hear a story, they make a project to help them remember the point of that lesson. Many of the craft projects are based on Bible verses which may be used as memory verses. Crafts include banners, a wind sock, greeting cards, boats, 3-D pictures, and much, much more.

If you are looking for short Bible stories with quick and easy follow-up crafts, this is the book for you!

TABLE OF CONTENTS

Shining Star Publications, Copyright © 1994

SS3809

DEDICATION

Dedicated to all those children I love, especially the ones who need to know that God loves them.

SS3809

GOD'S MERCY IN THE BIG FLOOD

Based on Genesis 6:11–9:17

Back in the days of Noah, there was much wickedness and violence on the earth. The people were doing things that were against God's will. God decided to get rid of the people because of their violence against Him.

Noah was the only person on earth who was honoring God, and God wanted to save him. He told Noah that He was going to destroy the earth with a flood. He told Noah to make an ark out of cypress wood. It was to be 450' long and 75' wide. That would make the ark longer than a football field but not quite as wide.

God told Noah to cover the ark with pitch, build on a roof, make three decks (lower, middle, and top), and put a door in one side. He also told Noah to bring his wife, his sons and their wives, and a male and female of every animal aboard the ark. This was to include birds and the things that crawl on the earth. Noah was also told to bring lots of food for the animals and the people.

SS3809

Noah did exactly as God had told him. Then the Lord shut him, his family, and the animals into the ark.

Noah was six hundred years old when the rain began. On the day he finished loading the ark, God shut him in and rain gushed down from the heavens. It rained for forty days and forty nights.

The whole face of the earth was flooded. Even the highest mountains were covered. Everything that lived on the earth died, even birds which usually fly above water did not survive that flood. The flood lasted 150 days.

Noah and his family took care of the animals for the whole trip. He finally sent a raven out of the ark to check on things. The raven flew around until the water had dried up and it could land.

After a while Noah sent out a dove. The dove came back. He waited seven more days, then sent the dove out again. Finally the dove came back. In its beak was a freshly picked olive leaf! This meant that the water had gone down enough for some treetops to be visible. Noah and his family were very happy.

Noah waited another seven days, then sent the dove out again. This time it didn't return. God had sent a wind and the waters were dried from off the earth. He told Noah, "Come out of the ark, you and your wife, and your sons and their wives. Bring out every kind of living creature that is with you–the birds, the animals, and all the creatures that move along the ground–so they can multiply on the earth."

Noah did as he was told. He built an altar to the Lord and burnt offerings on it.

God told Noah that He would never again flood the entire earth. As a sign of that promise, He put a rainbow in the sky for Noah and for the rest of us too. Next time we see a rainbow, let's think of God's promise and His mercy to Noah and to us. We wouldn't be here today if long, long ago God hadn't saved a few people from that flood.

CRAFT

To complete the picture of Noah and the flood, you will need:

- Crayons
- Scissors

1. Color the picture below. Color the back of bottom portion blue.
2. Cut off, where shown, at bottom of page.
3. Fold "water" up to cover the "land."

Cut off this area.

A SPECIAL BABY

Based on Genesis 18:1-15; 21:1-3

Abraham was a very old man. His wife, Sarah, was also old. She was too old to have children. This was a problem for both of them because they loved children and Abraham wanted sons and daughters and grandchildren.

God had told Abraham he would become the father of many nations, even kings. But Abraham was ninety-nine years old. Surely it was too late to have children!

A few days later Abraham was sitting in front of his tent among some trees. He looked up and saw three men. Abraham was a courteous man. He didn't know who they were, but he bowed and said, "If I have found favor in your eyes, my lord, do not pass your servant by. Let a little water be brought, and then you may all wash your feet and rest under this tree. Let me get you something to eat, so you can be refreshed."

He rushed into the tent to Sarah, his wife. He said, "Quick, get three measures of fine flour and knead it, and bake some bread." He then rushed out to his herd and found a calf, tender and good, and gave it to a servant who hurried to prepare it.

When the food was ready, Abraham brought it with curds and milk and gave it to the visitors. He stood by, under a tree, while they ate.

When they were done eating, they asked, "Where is Sarah, your wife?" By then, Abraham believed that the men were from God.

"She is in the tent," said Abraham.

"I will surely return to you about this time next year," one said. "Sarah, your wife, will have a son." The one who said this was actually the Lord! Sarah was listening just inside the tent. She laughed to herself because she was an old woman. Women can't have babies when they are old.

The Lord asked Abraham, "Why did Sarah laugh? Is anything too hard for the Lord? I will return to you at the appointed time next year and Sarah will have a son."

As the Lord had promised, Sarah had a son, Isaac. It was through Isaac that Abraham became the father of many nations, and some of his descendants were even kings.

CRAFT

To complete the promise banner, you will need:

- Drinking straw
- Crayons
- Scissors
- Glue
- String or yarn

1. Color the banner on the right.
2. Cut out on bold lines.
3. Cut drinking straw to about 7" length.
4. Wrap the top of the banner around the straw and glue in place.
5. Cut an 18" length of string.
6. Tie onto the straw for a hanger as illustrated.

Red
Orange
Yellow
Blue
Purple

GOD KEEPS HIS PROMISES

"Is anything too hard for the Lord?"
Genesis 18:14a

SS3809

THE RAM

Based on Genesis 22:1-14

Abraham loved God—a lot. He was an old man, but he had a young son, a little boy whom he also loved a great deal. The boy, Isaac, was his only child. God tested Abraham's love for Him by telling Abraham to take Isaac to the wilderness and offer him as a sacrifice.

Abraham cut some wood for the fire; then he called Isaac and two servants to go with him into the wilderness. Isaac said, "Father? The fire and the wood are here, but where is the lamb for the burnt offering?"

"God will provide it," Abraham told him.

When they got where they were going, Abraham laid out the wood for a fire. He picked up his knife. At that moment he heard God's voice: "Abraham, Abraham."

"Here I am," Abraham said.

"Do not lay a hand on the boy. Do not do anything to him," God said. "Now I know that you fear God because you have not withheld from me your only son."

Abraham looked around. There behind him, he saw a ram caught by its horns in a thicket. Abraham took the ram and offered it as a burnt offering instead of his son.

Abraham named that place "The Lord will provide."

God spared Abraham's son that day. He also spared us by sending His own Son to die for our sins. He is a wonderful, loving God!

SS3809

CRAFT

To complete the 3-D picture, you will need:

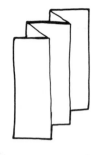

- Crayons
- Scissors

1. Color the picture below.

2. Cut out on bold lines.

3. Fanfold on dotted lines.

4. Stand on its edge. Look at it from the left side, and then to see a different picture, look at it from the right side.

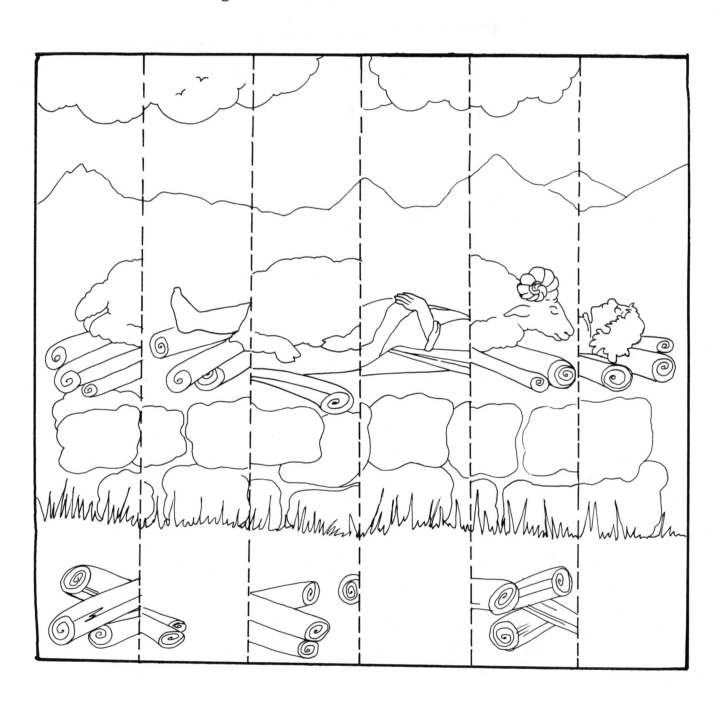

REBEKAH AT THE WELL

Based on Genesis 24:1-67

Abraham was an old man; God had blessed him in every way. God had promised him that He would make Abraham the father of many nations!

Abraham was getting worried though. His wife, Sarah, was dead and the only family member he had was his son, Isaac. God had promised him many descendants but Isaac wasn't even married yet. Abraham called his oldest and most trusted servant. He told him that he wanted Isaac to marry a girl from his own tribe. He instructed his servant to go to his hometown and find a bride for Isaac.

The servant wanted to please Abraham so he went to Nahor, the town where Abraham's relatives lived. He was worried about finding the right wife for Isaac. After he and his caravan had entered the city gates, he made the camels stop at the well. The young girls of the city went to the well every evening to get water for their families.

The servant knelt in prayer and asked for God's help. "I want to find a good wife for Abraham's son, Isaac," he said, "but I need a sign to guide me. I will ask the girls coming for water to dip some water for me. Let the girl You choose for Isaac be the one who agrees to get me a drink and also offers to water my camels."

The first girl to come to the well was lovely. The servant said to her, "Please give me a little water from your jar."

The girl answered him, "Drink, my lord," and she gave him water. Then she said, "I will draw water for your camels, too, until they have finished drinking."

This was the girl! Her name was Rebekah. Her family agreed that she could go with the servant and become the wife of Isaac.

The servant took her home. This made both Abraham and Isaac very happy. Rebekah was happy too. She was a good wife and she and her husband loved each other.

SS3809

CRAFT

To complete the wind sock, you will need:

- Crayons
- Scissors
- Glue
- Hole punch
- String

1. Color the pattern below.
2. Cut out on bold lines.
3. Apply glue on tab.
4. Roll pattern to form a tube shape and glue together.

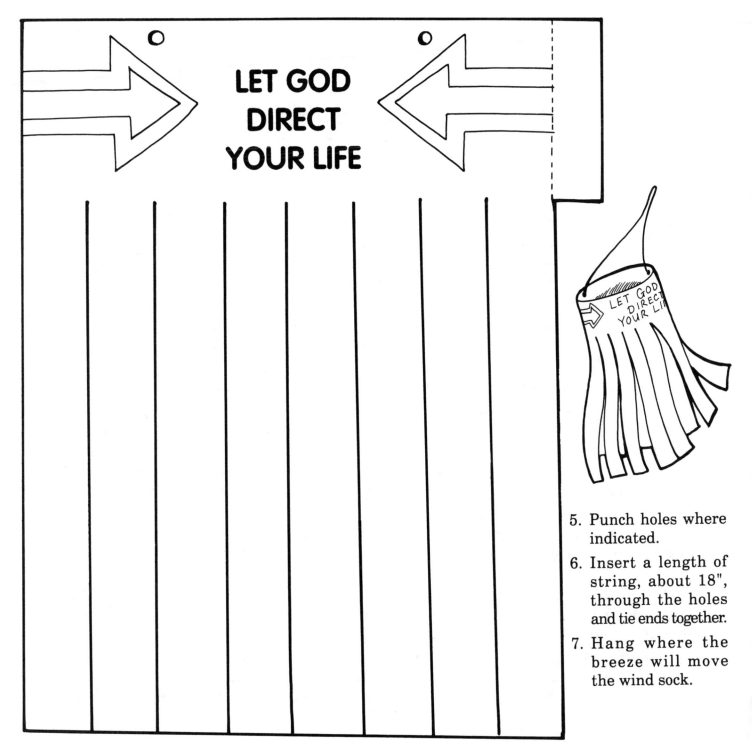

LET GOD
DIRECT
YOUR LIFE

5. Punch holes where indicated.
6. Insert a length of string, about 18", through the holes and tie ends together.
7. Hang where the breeze will move the wind sock.

SS3809

JOSEPH AND HIS BROTHERS

Based on Genesis 37; 42; 45

A long time ago in Israel, there were twelve brothers. They were the sons of a man named Jacob. They all herded their father's sheep.

One boy's name was Joseph. Jacob loved Joseph very much and gave him a fancy coat of many colors. Joseph was a dreamer. His brothers didn't like him because he told them about his dreams. They knew their father loved Joseph best and they were jealous of him.

One day the brothers plotted to kill Joseph. One brother who didn't want to kill him said, "Let's just throw him in this hole and leave him here." He planned to come back later and take Joseph out of the hole.

The brothers threw Joseph into the hole, then sat down to eat lunch.

While they were eating, a caravan of Ishmaelites came by. One brother suggested that selling Joseph to the Ishmaelites would be a good way to get rid of him. So they sold Joseph to the men in the caravan.

"Let's kill a goat and put its blood on Joseph's coat," said the brothers. "We can tell Father a wild animal killed him." Jacob was very sad when he was told that his beloved son Joseph had been killed.

Joseph was taken to Egypt and sold into slavery. Years passed and with God's help he worked his way out of slavery. He even became a very important man in the Egyptian court.

A famine hit the land of Israel. Jacob sent his sons to Egypt to try to buy food. When the brothers arrived in Egypt, they had to deal with an important man in Pharaoh's court—Joseph! Although Joseph recognized his brothers, they did not recognize him.

The brothers made several trips to Egypt to buy food, but Joseph did not tell them who he was. Finally one day he sent his servants from the room and told his brothers, "I am Joseph!" He told them that he forgave them because it was God's plan that he should be in Egypt.

SS3809

CRAFT

To complete the puzzle, you will need:

- Crayons
- Scissors
- Glue
- Thin cardboard (such as a used cereal box)

1. Color the circle below.

2. Spread an even layer of glue on a piece of cardboard slightly larger than the circle. Lay the circle carefully on the cardboard and press it down evenly and firmly.

3. When dry, cut out on outer edge. Cut apart on dotted lines to make a puzzle.

4. When not using the puzzle, store pieces in an envelope.

SS3809

LITTLE BOAT IN THE REEDS

Based on Exodus 2:1-10

Back in the days when the Israelites were slaves in Egypt, the rulers of Egypt were called pharaohs. One of the pharaohs hated the Israelites so much, he gave an order that all their male babies were to be thrown into the Nile River to drown.

One Israelite woman who had a baby boy could not bear to see her child hurt, so she hid him until he was three months old. She worried that he would be found and killed. She would also be punished, probably with death, if the pharaoh's soldiers found her baby.

One day she made a little boat–like a basket. Pharaoh had said to put boy babies into the Nile and she would–in a little boat! She placed the little boat, containing her baby, into the river among the reeds.

When Pharaoh's daughter went down to the river with her handmaidens, she saw the basket-boat and sent one of her handmaidens to get it. When she saw the Israelite baby she decided to keep him for her own. She named him Moses.

Moses was treated well by the daughter of Pharaoh and was an important person in Pharaoh's household. He grew up in Egypt, but when he became a man Moses left. Later he led the Israelites out of slavery in Egypt to freedom.

SS3809

CRAFT

To complete the baby in a basket-boat, you will need:

- Crayons
- Scissors
- Glue

1. Color the fronts and backs of the pieces on this page.
2. Cut out on bold lines.
3. Fold on dotted lines.
4. Apply glue to tabs and fasten, where shown, to form a basket-boat.
5. Lay baby in basket.

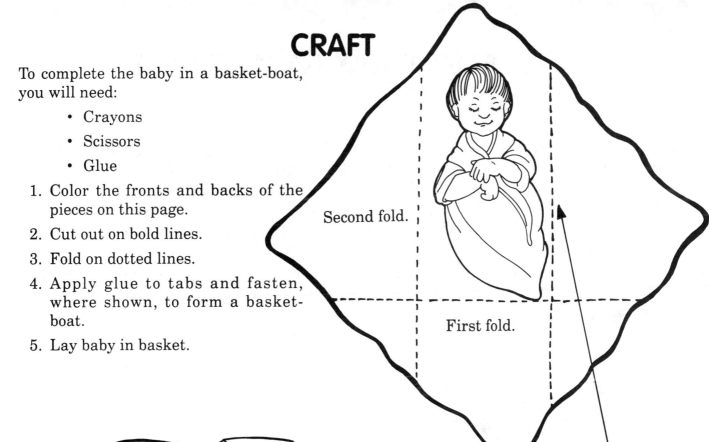

Second fold.

First fold.

Third fold—to form a blanket around the baby.

Basket

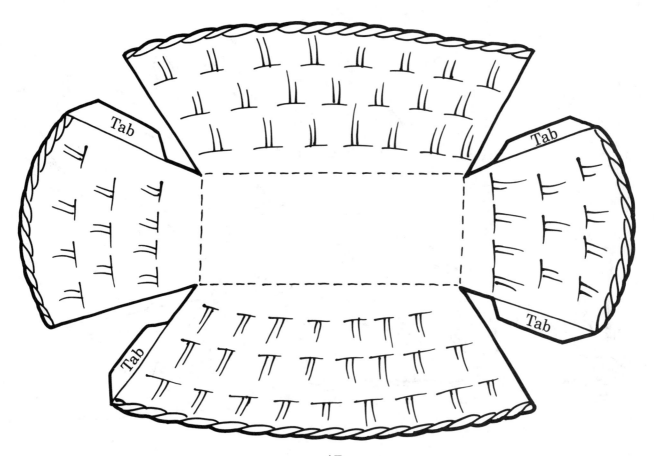

SS3809

A STRANGE WAY TO MEET GOD

Based on Exodus 3:1-4:21

When Moses grew to be a man he got in trouble in Egypt. He saw an Egyptian beating an Israelite. He was so angry that he killed the Egyptian. He ran away to the land of Midian to hide from the soldiers who would be looking for him.

He married and began tending the flocks of his father-in-law. One day Moses was walking along when a bush nearby burst into flame. The bush was not burned but the flame kept burning. This was an unusual sight, so he decided to take a closer look.

As he walked nearer he heard a voice. "Moses! Moses!" The voice was coming from the bush.

"Here I am," said Moses.

SS3809

"Do not come any closer. Take off your sandals, for the place where you are standing is holy ground." It was the voice of God! He said, "I am the God of your father, the God of Abraham, the God of Isaac, and the God of Jacob." Moses took off his sandals and hid his face. He was afraid to look at God.

God said, "I have indeed seen the misery of my people in Egypt. I have heard them crying out because of their slave drivers, and I am concerned about their suffering. So I have come down to rescue them from the hands of the Egyptians and to bring them out of that land into a good and spacious land, a land flowing with milk and honey. I am sending you to Pharaoh to bring my people the Israelites out of Egypt."

"Who am I, that I should go to Pharaoh and bring the Israelites out of Egypt?" Moses pleaded.

"I will be with you," said God. "And this will be a sign to you that it is I who have sent you. When you have brought the people out of Egypt, you will worship God on this mountain."

They talked for a while; then Moses worried aloud, "Oh Lord, I am slow of speech and tongue."

"Go," said God. "I will help you speak and will teach you what to say. What about your brother, Aaron? He is already on his way to meet you and his heart will be glad when he sees you. You shall speak to him and put words in his mouth; I will help both of you speak. It will be as if he were your mouth and as if you were God to him." Then God told Moses to take a staff in his hand so he could perform miraculous signs with it.

Moses went back to Egypt. He led the Israelites out of their slavery and into the Promised Land.

SS3809

CRAFT

To complete the burning bush, you will need:

- Crayons
- Scissors
- Hole punch
- Brad fastener

1. Color the bush and wheel using the color chart below.

2. Cut out on bold lines.

3. Use a hole punch to punch out all the black circles on the bush.

4. Placing the colored wheel behind the bush, insert a brad fastener in the center hole of the bush, and then into the center hole of the colored wheel. Open the fastener to secure.

5. Spin the colored wheel to make the bush "burn."

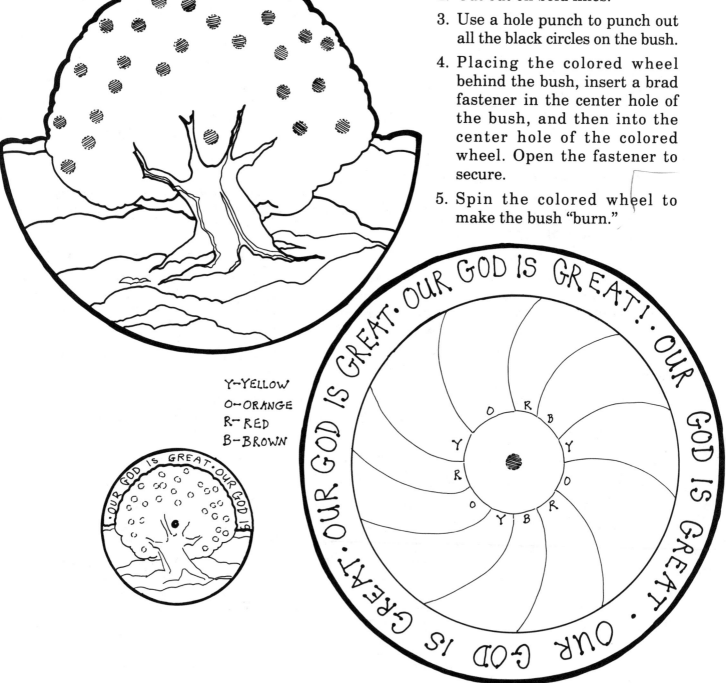

Y—YELLOW
O—ORANGE
R—RED
B—BROWN

THE VERY STRONG MAN
Based on Judges 13:24-16:30

During the time when the Israelites were conquered by the Philistines a special baby was born. His parents were told by an angel of God that he would free Israel. His hair was never to be cut. The baby's name was Samson, and he grew up to be a very strong man.

After Samson was married, he often fought the Philistines and defeated them. They were afraid of him. To get even with Samson the Philistines came to his wife and asked her the secret of Samson's strength, but he had not told her even though she had asked him. She was afraid but couldn't say what his secret was, so they killed her and her father.

                                                                      SS3809

In anger Samson killed more Philistines. They went to find him to put him in prison. When they found him, Samson picked up the jawbone of a burro, lying on the ground, and killed one thousand Philistine men. Then he thanked God for helping and saving him.

One day Samson met a woman named Delilah. She was not a good person and was friendly with the Philistines. She talked Samson into telling her the secret of his strength. He told her that if his hair was cut, he would lose his strength and be like any other man.

The Philistines paid Delilah one thousand pieces of silver to help them cut Samson's hair. When he went to sleep with his head on her lap, she called a man with a razor. The man cut off Samson's hair and all his strength left him.

The Philistines caught him–he only had ordinary strength left–and put out his eyes. They made him grind grain at the prison mill. A little later they took him to their temple for a special celebration. They stood him among the pillars of the temple so everyone could see him and laugh at him. The temple and the pillar he was bound to were made of stone and very sturdy.

Because Samson was blind, he asked a servant who was there to help him feel the pillars supporting the temple. He said he needed to lean on them. The leaders of the Philistines were in the temple that day, along with many people. And three thousand men and women were on the roof watching Samson.

Samson prayed and asked God to give him all his strength back so he could pull down the pillars and kill the Philistines. "Let me die with the Philistines," he prayed.

God gave him back his strength, and Samson pushed with all his might. The pillars came down and so did the temple. Samson died, but so did all those Philistines who were making life so hard for the Israelites.

CRAFT

To complete the friendly letter, you will need:

- Crayons
- Scissors
- Postage stamp
- Glue
- Pencil

1. Color the pattern below.

2. Cut out on bold lines.

3. Fold on dotted lines. Write your letter on the blank side. Write to a friend about how God cares for us. Add your return address on the short lines. Write the name and address of your friend on the longer lines. Seal letter by applying glue in oval area and folding over. Apply a first-class stamp in area shown.

SS3809

THE BOY IN THE TEMPLE

Based on 1 Samuel 3:4-21

"Samuel, Samuel."

"Here I am," said the boy Samuel, as he ran into the place where Eli, the priest, was sleeping.

"I did not call you; go back and lie down," said Eli. Samuel went back to bed.

Then he heard, "Samuel, Samuel."

"Here I am; you called me," said Samuel, as he ran again to where Eli was sleeping.
"I did not call; go back and lie down."

SS3809

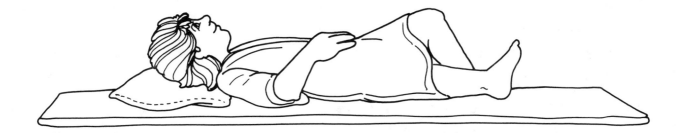

A third time the voice spoke: "Samuel, Samuel."

Samuel ran again to Eli. "Here I am," he said, "you called me."

Eli understood then that it was the Lord who was calling the boy. "That was God calling you," he said. "Go and lie down. If He calls you say, 'Speak, Lord, for your servant is listening.'"

Samuel went back to his bed. "Samuel! Samuel!" came the voice.

"Speak, Lord, for your servant is listening," said Samuel.

The Lord said to Samuel, "I am about to do a thing in Israel that will make the ears of everyone who hears of it tingle. At that time I will carry out against Eli everything I have spoken against his house. His sons made themselves contemptible, and he failed to restrain them."

Samuel lay in his bed worrying until morning. He was a helper in the house of the Lord. In the morning he opened the doors as he was supposed to. Then Eli called to him, "Samuel, my son."

Samuel was afraid. He didn't want to tell Eli what the Lord had said, but he answered, "Here I am."

Eli could see that Samuel was embarrassed and didn't want to tell, so he said, "What was it that God said to you? Do not hide it from me."

Even though he was afraid, Samuel told Eli what God had told him. Eli said, "He is the Lord; let him do what is good in his eyes." He wasn't angry at Samuel at all.

As Samuel grew up, the Lord was with him. The Lord made him a great prophet of Israel.

CRAFT

To complete the Samuel doll, you will need:

- Crayons
- Scissors
- Brad fastener

1. Color pieces A and B.

2. Cut out on bold lines.

3. Insert a brad fastener through the figure of Samuel where the black dot is and then through the black dot in the temple scene.

4. Move the boy's body to sit up or lie down.

A

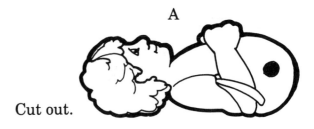

Cut out.

B

Here I am, Lord.
I will obey You.

SS3809

DAVID AND THE SLING

Based on 1 Samuel 17

David picked up the package of food he was taking to his brothers and grabbed his sling in case he needed it. He was very good with the sling. As a shepherd boy he had used it to kill lions wanting to harm his sheep.

The sling wasn't a slingshot of the kind children use today. It was a weapon made of two leather thongs tied to a pouch to hold a rock. To use it, David put a rock in the pouch and swung it by the long thongs. When he let go of one of the thongs, the rock would fly toward what he wanted to hit–like a bullet. He felt safe with his sling.

After a long walk, David got to where his brothers were with Saul's army. "Father sent you some food," he told his brothers. "He says you'll be needing it."

The brothers eagerly tore open the package. "That's wonderful," they said. "We were hungry!"

Shining Star Publications, Copyright © 1994 SS3809

At that moment an extremely frightening warrior, a giant of a man, came forward from the Philistine army. He was wearing heavy, bronze armor and a helmet. He shouted, "Choose a man and have him come down to me. If he is able to fight and kill me, we will become your servants, but if I overcome him and kill him you will become our subjects and serve us."

David swung his sling, thinking. He went to see King Saul. David said to him, "Let no one lose heart on account of this Philistine; your servant will go and fight him."

Saul said to David, "Go, and the Lord be with you."

David picked up five smooth, round rocks. He put one into the pouch of his sling. He prayed as he walked toward the giant. Goliath roared with laughter. "Am I a dog that you come at me with sticks?" he asked. He raised his great spear, with the shining sharp point, and walked toward David.

David continued walking forward, too, swinging his sling at his side. "I come against you in the name of the Lord Almighty; the God of the armies of Israel," he said.

As David got closer he swung the sling around and around, faster and faster. Goliath ran toward him, his terrible spear still raised and ready to throw. David let go of one of the thongs of his sling.

Whump! It wasn't a very loud noise, but Goliath stopped. His body fell to earth. Clang! His armor hit the ground. The small rock had hit him right between the eyes.

David walked quietly forward and looked down at the giant. Then he quietly prayed and thanked God for helping him defeat the giant.

When the Israelite army saw that the giant was dead, they began to chase the Philistine army. With God's help, David, a shepherd boy, had won the battle!

To complete the door hanger, you will need: **CRAFT**
- Light cardboard or poster board
- Cotton ball   1. Color the door hanger below. Glue it to light cardboard or poster board.
- Crayons   2. Cut out on bold lines.
- Scissors   3. Fold on dotted lines and cut out where indicated.
- Glue   4. Use glue to fasten both sides together and to attach cotton ball to sheep.

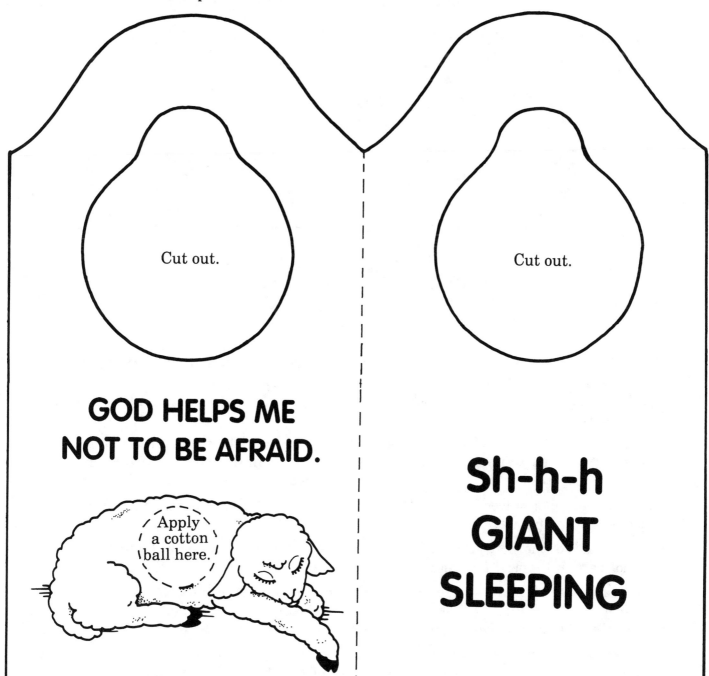

Cut out.

Cut out.

GOD HELPS ME NOT TO BE AFRAID.

Apply a cotton ball here.

Sh-h-h GIANT SLEEPING

"For the battle is not yours, but God's."
2 Chronicles 20:15b

AHAB AND THE IDOLS
Based on 1 Kings 16:29-17:6

Ahab, the king of Israel, was having a wonderful time. He called in the man who worked in gold. He told him to make an idol for Baal. He called in the workers in silver and told them to make a silver idol. Then he called in all the carpenters he knew. He had them to make some wooden idols.

When all his idols were made, they were set up in his palace and in the courtyard. Some of the less important ones were put in the marketplace. Everyone was encouraged to kneel before the gods and pray to them.

One day a prophet of God named Elijah came to see the king. Ahab asked him what he was doing in the palace.

Elijah said, "As the Lord, the God of Israel, lives, whom I serve, there will be neither dew nor rain in the next few years except at my word."

Many days passed. Ahab waited for rain, and waited, and waited. Streams were drying up. Crops were dying. Ahab was very angry at Elijah. He blamed the drought on Elijah. He sent soldiers looking for the prophet.

Knowing that there would be trouble, God had told Elijah to go away and hide in a special place in the wilderness. God took care of him by sending ravens that brought Elijah bread and meat in the morning and evening, and he was able to drink from the brook.

SS3809

CRAFT

To complete the 3-D bird (raven), you will need:

- Crayons
- Scissors
- Glue
- Hole punch
- 12"-18" length of string

1. Color the bird black.
2. Cut out on bold lines.
3. Fold on dotted line.
4. Punch holes where indicated.
5. Tie string between the wings to balance bird when hanging up.

* Glue the "piece of food" in bird's bill.

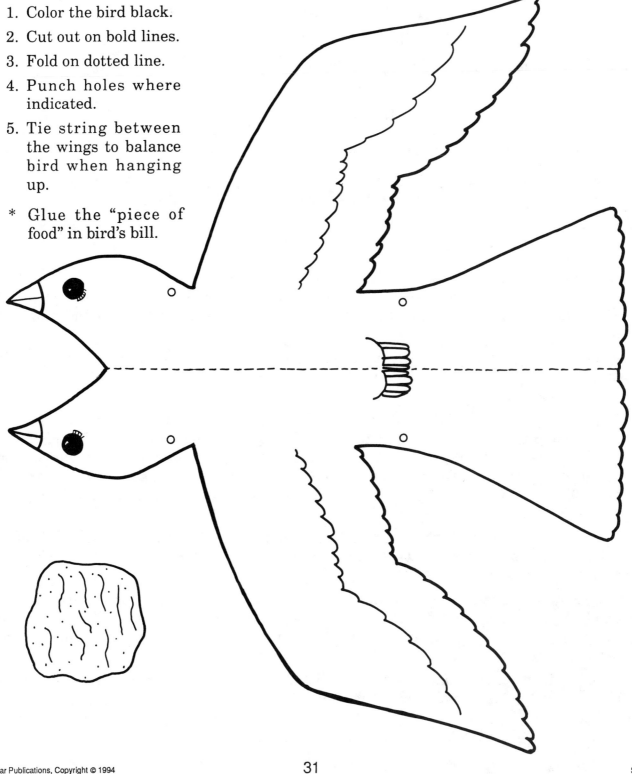

THE FLOUR AND THE OIL

Based on 1 Kings 17:8-16

God told His prophet Elijah to warn King Ahab to stop worshiping idols. Elijah told Ahab that his punishment would be a drought in the land–no rain for three years! Then God sent Elijah to a place of safety where ravens brought him food and he had plenty of water to drink.

After a while, the creek Elijah was drinking from dried up and he had to leave. God told him, "Go at once to Zarephath. I have commanded a widow in that place to supply you with food."

Elijah went. It was a long walk to Zarephath and he became very thirsty. He was anxious to find the widow God had told him about. When he finally got to Zarephath he saw a woman gathering sticks for a fire. Elijah thought she must be the widow God had sent him to find. "Would you bring me a little water in a jar so that I may have a drink?" he asked her. As she was leaving to do what he asked, he also said, "Bring me please, a piece of bread."

"I don't have any bread," she told him, "only a handful of flour in a jar and a little oil. I am gathering a few sticks to take home and make a meal for myself and my son, that we may eat it–and die."

"Don't be afraid," said Elijah, "make a small cake of bread for me from what you have and bring it to me, and then make something for yourself and your son. The Lord God of Israel has promised that the jar of flour will not be used up and the jug of oil will not run dry until the day the Lord gives rain on the land." And it was so.

Both the flour and oil lasted as long as Elijah, the widow, and her son needed them. It was a miracle. God is great and wonderful!

SS3809

CRAFT

To complete this picture, you will need:

- Crayons
- Scissors
- Brad fastener

1. Color the two pieces.
2. Cut out on bold lines.
3. Insert brad fastener through the black dot in the picture and then through the center of the wheel.
4. Turn the wheel to see food on the table.

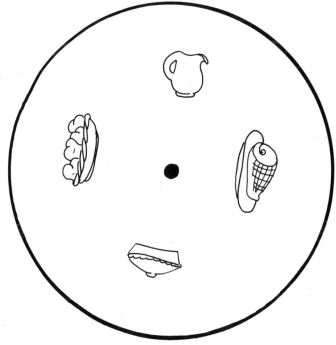

SS3809

THE HEALING POWER OF GOD

Based on 1 Kings 17:17-24

A widow and her son gave Elijah a place to live in their home. God provided food for all three of them while there was a drought in the land.

One day the widow's son became sick and died. The widow said to Elijah, "What do you have against me, man of God? Did you come to remind me of my sin and kill my son?"

"Give me your son," Elijah said. He carried the boy to his upstairs bedroom. He laid the boy on his bed. Then he cried out to the Lord, "Oh Lord my God, have you brought tragedy upon this widow I am staying with by letting her son die?"

Elijah stretched himself out over the boy three times and cried out again, "Oh Lord my God, let this boy's life return to him!" God heard Elijah's prayer and the boy revived.

Elijah carried him downstairs.

"Look," he told the boy's mother, "your son is alive!"

The woman said to Elijah, "Now I know that you are a man of God and that the word of the Lord from your mouth is the truth."

SS3809

CRAFT

To complete the poster, you will need:

- Markers or crayons
- Scissors
- Gold and silver glitter
- Glue

1. Color and cut out.
2. Decorate with gold and silver glitter.

JONAH ON THE BEACH

Based on Jonah 1:1-3:3a

The word of God came to a prophet named Jonah. God told him to go to Nineveh and tell the people to mend their wicked ways.

Jonah didn't want to go, he thought the people of Nineveh deserved punishment from God, and he was just scared. He went instead to the seaport and got on a ship bound for Tarshish in the opposite direction.

The ship set out and everything went along fine. Suddenly a great storm came up. Everyone on the ship was afraid. Jonah told the crew that he was a prophet who feared the Lord, but he was running away from what God had told him to do. He explained that this might be why the storm had arisen. "Pick me up and throw me into the sea," Jonah said, "and it will become calm."

The crew became even more afraid. They thought God would sink their ship. They did their best to row back to land. But the sea grew even wilder.

SS3809

The men cried out, "Lord, please do not let us die for taking this man's life." Then they threw Jonah off the ship. Immediately the storm stopped. The waters became calm. But the Lord provided a great big fish to swallow Jonah. He was inside the fish for three days and nights.

Jonah prayed for deliverance all the time he was inside the fish. After three days the fish spat him out on the beach. Jonah walked off toward Nineveh, making wet, squishy sounds as he walked. He had learned an important lesson: when God tells you what to do, you'd better do it!

Shining Star Publications, Copyright © 1994   SS3809

CRAFT

To make a boat follow these instructions. You will need a piece of paper and pencil.

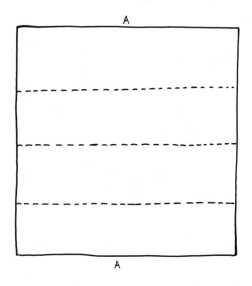

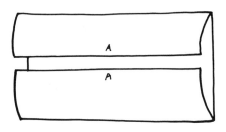

1. Fold a square piece of paper in half; then unfold. Label sides A and fold toward center.

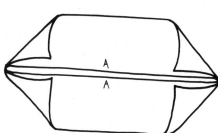

2. Fold end flaps toward the center.

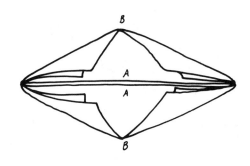

3. Fold again.

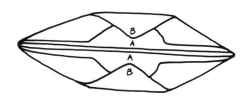

4. Label points B and fold toward center.

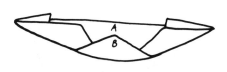

5. Fold paper back in half on center fold.

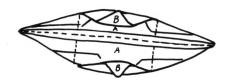

6. Take hold of the areas marked A. Pull outward slightly, holding points B and turn inside out.

7. Smooth out with your fingers to make the boat sit evenly on a flat surface. Erase the A and B pencil marks.

AN ANGEL VISITS MARY

Based on Luke 1:26-38

Mary was a young woman who lived in the town of Nazareth. One day she had an important visitor–the angel Gabriel. "Greetings, you who are highly favored! The Lord is with you," he said.

Mary was surprised and troubled at this greeting given to her by an angel of God. She wondered what it could mean.

Gabriel went on, "Do not be afraid, Mary, you have found favor with God. You will be with child and give birth to a son, and you are to give him the name Jesus. He will be great and will be called the Son of the Most High. The Lord God will give him the throne of his father, David, and he will reign over the house of Jacob forever, and his Kingdom will never end."

Mary wondered, "How can this be?" for she had no husband.

The angel told Mary that God would be the baby's father. Then Gabriel told her that her cousin Elizabeth, in her old age, was also expecting a son, for nothing is impossible with God.

Mary smiled and said, "I am the Lord's servant. May it be as you have said."

Gabriel left, and Mary had much to think about.

                                                          SS3809

CRAFT

To complete the stand-up angel, you will need:

- Markers or crayons
- Scissors
- Glue

1. Color the angel.

2. Cut out on bold lines.

3. Apply glue on tab.

4. Roll skirt area to fasten into cone shape.

Apply glue here.

SS3809

THE STABLE

Based on Luke 2:1-20

A young man named Joseph walked into town leading a burro on which his wife, Mary, was riding. He was very tired. She was going to have a baby. Joseph led the burro to an inn and went in to rent a room.

"Sorry," said the innkeeper, "all my rooms are full. There are many people here to be counted for the census. We have no rooms to rent." Joseph looked out the door. Mary was leaning on the burro looking very tired and sick.

"Is that your wife?" asked the innkeeper.

"Yes," said Joseph. "She's expecting a baby."

"I am sorry I don't have a room," said the innkeeper, "but I do have one place you can stay. It isn't much, just a stable. It's out back in the pasture. At least it has a roof and walls to keep out the cold wind, and the animals there will provide a little heat."

"Thank you," said Joseph.

Mary got back on the burro and Joseph led the animal to the stable. He put the burro into a stall. Mary lay down with the smell of fresh hay and the sound of farm animals all around.

A little later her baby was born. Both Mary and Joseph were very happy to see Him. "Hello, Jesus. You are a beautiful baby," said Mary. She wrapped Him in a small blanket she had brought and laid Him in a manger full of sweet-smelling hay.

Sometime later several shepherds arrived. One of them asked, "May we come in and see the newborn Christ Child? An angel told us He was here."

Joseph let the men come in and look at the newborn Messiah. The shepherds bowed and worshiped the baby.

CRAFT

To complete the stable, you will need:

- Markers or crayons
- Scissors
- Glue

1. Color the pictures.
2. Cut out on the bold lines.
3. Fold on dotted lines.
4. Glue the top of the roof as shown. Glue the Mary and Joseph figure in the middle of the stable.

Finished picture

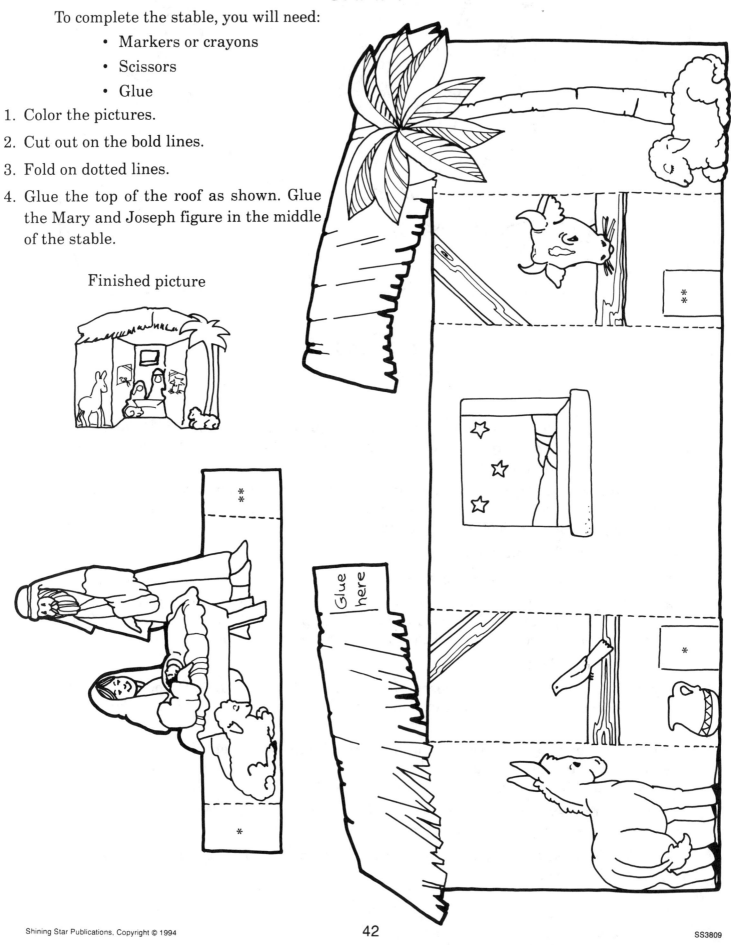

THE STAR

Based on Matthew 2:1-12

The three wise men had traveled a long way following a star to the newborn Christ Child. When they got to Jerusalem, they decided to stop and ask for further directions.

They arrived at the palace and asked to see King Herod. They asked him if he knew where the King of the Jews was to be born.

King Herod had heard of the birth of a new king and he was worried. He was afraid Jesus would lead the Israelites away from his rule, and he would lose his money and power. He wanted to kill Baby Jesus. "Follow your star to the newborn Christ Child," he said. "Then come and tell me exactly where He is. I want to worship Him too."

The wise men agreed; then they got on their camels and rode off toward Bethlehem where the Old Testament said Jesus would be born.

SS3809

The star led them to a small stable in Bethlehem. When the wise men saw Jesus, they got off their camels and knelt in worship.

They had brought special gifts with them. The gifts were gold, incense, and myrrh. Mary and Joseph were pleased at such wonderful gifts for their child.

The wise men left, but they did not go back by way of Jerusalem. God warned them in a dream to avoid Herod, so they took another route home.

They were overjoyed that God had allowed them to see His Son.

SS3809

CRAFT

To complete the star, you will need the following:

- Markers or crayons
- Scissors
- Glue
- Hole punch
- Thread or yarn

1. Color the points of the star yellow.
2. Cut out on bold lines.
3. Fold on dotted lines.

4. Apply glue on the tab and fasten to area *.
5. Apply glue behind points and fasten as shown.
6. Cut out the message pentagon on the right and glue it on the front of the star.
7. Punch a hole in the star point where the black dot is and insert a 10" piece of thread to tie into a loop. Hang the star.

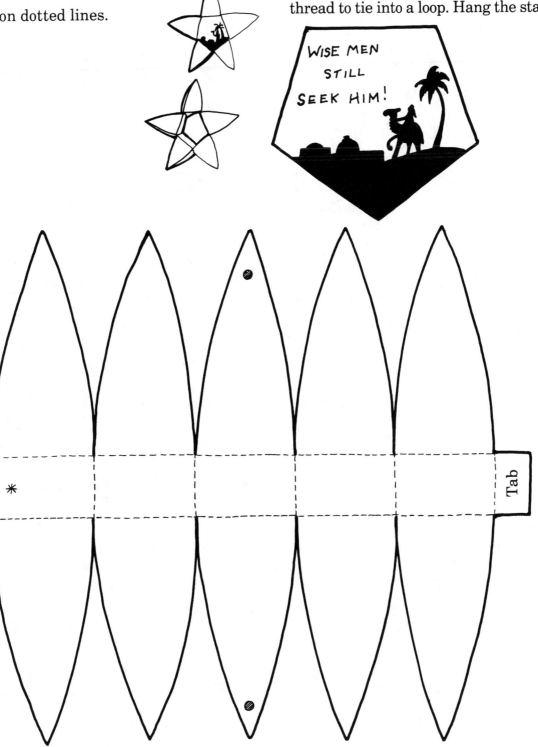

WISE MEN STILL SEEK HIM!

SS3809

THE BAD KING
Based on Matthew 2:7-15

For hundreds of years the Jews had expected a Messiah. They had read prophesies in the Old Testament telling what He would be like. Christ means "Great General and Wonderful King." They thought this meant that He would save them from the ungodly people who ruled them.

When Jesus was born, Herod was king. He was afraid that this Messiah who was to be born would lead the people away from him, and he couldn't be king anymore. He worried and worried.

When the wise men came to his palace asking about the Christ Child, Herod saw his chance. He told them to let him know when they found the Christ Child because he wanted to go worship Him too. That was a lie! Herod wanted to know where Jesus was so he could send soldiers to kill Him.

God had a plan to save Jesus. After the wise men worshiped Jesus and gave Him gifts of gold, incense, and myrrh they went home another way. God warned them in a dream not to see Herod.

After the wise men left, Joseph also had a dream. An angel of the Lord came to him and told him, "Get up, take the child and his mother and escape to Egypt. Stay there until I tell you, for Herod is going to search for the child to kill him."

Joseph got right up and told Mary to get up and get the child. They hurriedly left for Egypt. Later, Herod looked all over for Jesus but didn't find Him. Herod was very angry.

Joseph didn't bring Mary and Jesus back to Israel until King Herod was dead. God's plan had worked. Jesus was safe!

SS3809

CRAFT

To complete the bear pencil holder, you will need:

- Crayons
- Glue
- Scissors
- 12-oz frozen juice can

1. Color the pattern on this page.
2. Cut out on bold lines.
3. Glue to the outside of the juice can.
4. Use to hold pencils and pens.

Apply glue here.

GOD
WILL
TAKE
CARE
OF YOU

SS3809

HIS FATHER'S HOUSE
Based on Luke 2:41-52

When Jesus was twelve years old, He and His family went to Jerusalem to celebrate Passover. Passover is a yearly festival to remember the time Moses led the Israelites out of slavery in Egypt. Every Jewish person celebrated that anniversary–and many still do.

Jesus' parents worshiped in the temple and celebrated with their friends at a Passover dinner. After the celebration had ended, they all left together. The young people traveled in a group, just for the fun of being with one another, and the adults walked together. They talked about the fine time they had enjoyed at Passover.

Finally, after they had traveled all day, Mary asked for Jesus. She didn't see Him. She asked the children about Him and went all through the group of traveling companions looking for her son. Jesus was not there! This frightened Mary. She went to find Joseph. "Where's Jesus?" she asked. "I can't find Him."

Joseph didn't know either, and that frightened Mary even more. "We must go back to Jerusalem. He's only twelve," she said. "I'm afraid my son is lost."

It took quite a while to get back to Jerusalem. When they got there, Mary and Joseph looked and looked for three days. No Jesus. Finally they went to the temple, hoping that He might be there. There He was, sitting among the teachers. All who listened were amazed at what a smart boy He was. His understanding and the questions He asked astonished the teachers.

Mary asked, "Son, why have you treated us like this? Your father and I have been anxiously searching for you."

Jesus replied, "Didn't you know I had to be in my Father's house?" Mary didn't understand the words of her son, but she remembered them and thought about them.

CRAFT

To complete this craft, you will need:

- Crayons
- Scissors
- Glue

1. Color the inside and outside of the church.
2. Cut out on bold lines including the center and top of door.
3. Glue piece A behind the door.
4. Fold door on dotted lines. Open door to see inside.

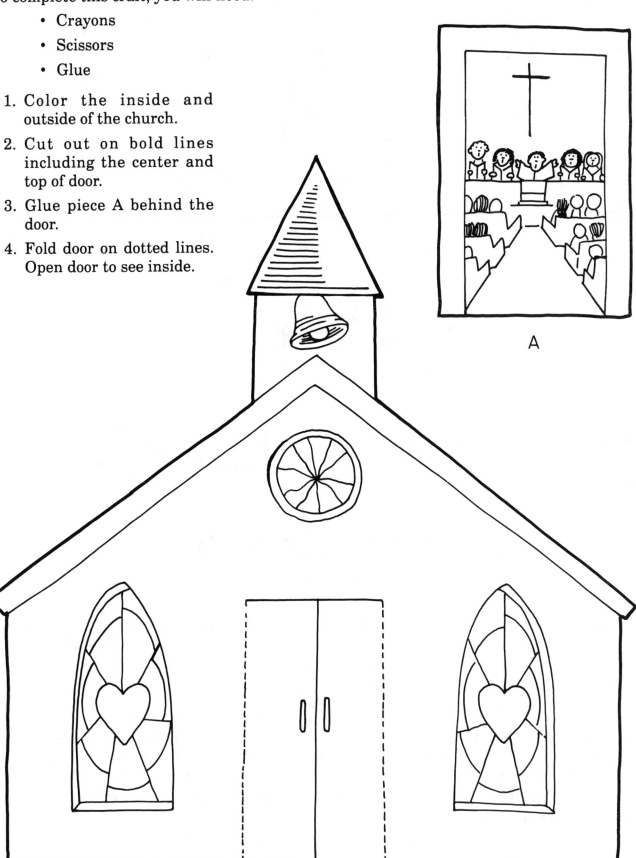

A

SS3809

JESUS IS BAPTIZED

Based on Matthew 3:13-17

One day John the Baptist was baptizing people in the Jordan River and preaching to the crowds. He looked up and saw Jesus walking toward the river. When He reached the river bank, Jesus said, "Good morning, John. It's time for you to baptize Me."

John replied, "I need to be baptized by You, and do You come to me?"

"Let it be so now; it is proper for us to do this to fulfill all righteousness," said Jesus.

He walked down into the river and John baptized Him. Suddenly the heavens were opened, and the Holy Spirit of God descended on Jesus in the shape of a dove. A voice from heaven said, "This is my Son, whom I love; with Him I am well pleased."

Everyone heard the wonderful voice. The God of all creation had placed His blessing on Jesus, His only Son.

CRAFT

To complete this sun catcher, you will need:

- Crayons
- Scissors
- Vegetable or salad oil
- Rags or paper towels
- String
- Hole punch

1. Color the pattern below. Use bright colors and press firmly with your crayons to produce even, solid color.

2. Cut out on outer line.

3. Use an old rag or paper towel to spread a small amount of oil on picture. Rub it over entire picture.

4. Use a clean rag or towel to rub off excess oil.

5. Use a hole punch to make a hole at the top where indicated.

6. Insert a short length of string to form a loop for hanging. Hang in a window and see how the light shines through.

SS3809

JESUS COMES TO DINNER

Based on Mark 2:13-17

One day as Jesus was walking by the lake teaching people about His Father, He saw a man named Levi sitting at a tax collector's booth. "Follow Me," Jesus said, and Levi got up and went with Him.

Later, Jesus and His disciples went to dinner at Levi's house. Levi had invited many tax collectors and sinners to the dinner. Some Pharisees said to Jesus' disciples, "Why does He eat with these sinners?"

These Pharisees thought they were too good to eat with "sinful people." But that's not how Jesus felt. He heard the question, and He replied, "Healthy people don't need a doctor but sick people do. I have not come to save righteous people but sinners."

SS3809

The Pharisees thought Jesus should have nothing to do with sinful people. But how would they learn about Jesus if He ignored them? Levi's life was changed when he met Jesus, and so were the lives of many others when they met Him.

Levi was also called Matthew. He became one of Jesus' disciples and wrote the first book in the New Testament.

SS3809

CRAFT

To complete this fish bookmark, you will need:

- Colored pencils or markers
- Scissors
- Yarn or string

1. Color the fish below with colored pencils or markers. (If you color with crayons, the color may transfer to the pages of the book you are marking.)

2. Cut out on bold lines.

3. Cut an 8" piece of yarn or string and glue one end inside the folded area of the Bible verse piece and the other end inside the mouth of the fish to look like a fishing line.

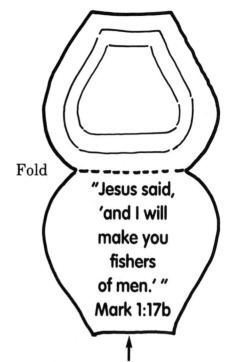

Fold

"Jesus said, 'and I will make you fishers of men.' " Mark 1:17b

Apply glue under this area; then lay one end of string inside and press.

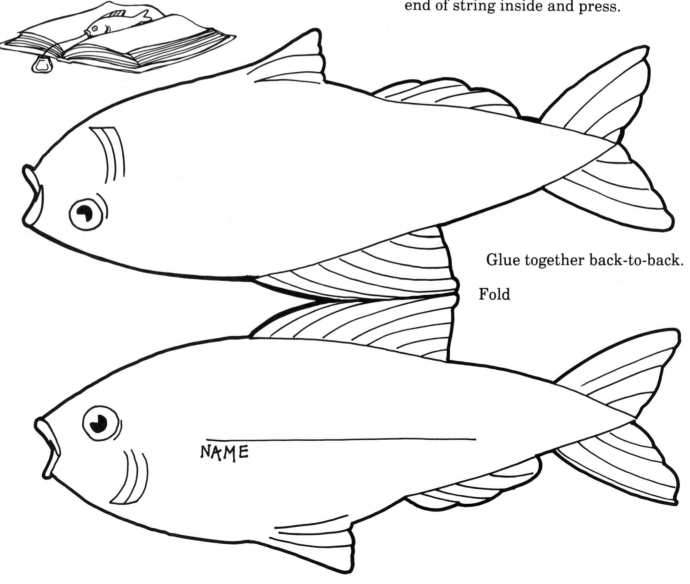

Glue together back-to-back.

Fold

NAME

THE SIMPLE FAITH OF A CHILD
Based on Mark 10:13-16

It was a beautiful, sunny day, not too hot even for Israel. Jesus was teaching a group of people about His Holy Father and Himself. Some parents were trying to get through the crowd to Him, because they wanted Him to bless their children. The children were probably noisy, as they sometimes are.

"Take those children away," said the disciples, "Jesus is busy!" They didn't want their Master bothered when He was doing important work.

The Lord looked at the children Himself and said, "Let the little children come to me, and do not hinder them, for the kingdom of God belongs to such as these. I tell you the truth, anyone who does not receive the kingdom of God like a little child will never enter it."

The parents were happy as the children smiled and went to Jesus. Lovingly, He took them in His arms, put His hands on them, and blessed each one.

 SS3809

CRAFT

To complete the 3-D picture frame, you will need:

- Crayons
- Scissors
- Glue
- Photo of child (optional)

1. Color the heart and flowers and cut them out.

2. Glue the cutout flowers on the flowers on the heart. Apply glue only under the flower centers, allowing the petals to stand out for a 3-D effect.

3. Draw your picture in the circle or glue a small photo of yourself there.

JESUS LOVES

SS3809

A DISCIPLE SHOULD BE LIKE HIS TEACHER

Based on Matthew 10:24-25

When John the Baptist baptized Jesus, the Father sent the Holy Spirit of God down from heaven like a dove to rest on Him. After His baptism, Jesus went into the wilderness for prayer and fasting.

It wasn't long after Jesus had come back from the wilderness that He began preparing to go from town to town, teaching and healing people and bringing them into the kingdom of God. He gathered His twelve disciples and sent them out in His name to teach and heal.

He gave them careful instructions for how they were to serve Him. If they weren't welcomed in a home they were to leave the house and even the town, after shaking the dust of the place from their feet.

Jesus told them something else, too, which is a lesson for all of us. He said, "A student is not above his teacher, nor a servant above his master. It is enough for the student to be like his teacher, and the servant like his master."

Jesus wants us to try our hardest to be loving and gentle, as He is. We can all try to do as Jesus told us. We can be gentle and loving and show our friends how followers of Jesus act. Maybe we can help bring people who don't know Him into His kingdom.

SS3809

CRAFT

To complete the fan, you will need:

- Crayons
- Scissors
- Glue
- Thin cardboard
  (such as a used cereal box)
- Craft stick

1. Color the pattern below.
2. Cut out on bold line.
3. Glue pattern to thin cardboard; then cut out again.
4. Glue a craft stick to the pattern for a handle.

A LESSON FOR JOHN THE BAPTIST
Based on Matthew 11:2-7

Herod, the king of Israel during the time Jesus was preaching and teaching, was a wicked man. When John the Baptist preached about repentance the king threw him into prison.

John knew that the Messiah was coming, but he was not totally sure who the Messiah was. Jesus was John's cousin and a great man. But John wasn't sure if his own cousin could be the Christ! He thought and thought about it and worried too.

While in prison, John sent two of his disciples to find Jesus to ask Him if He was the Christ.

When the men found Jesus they asked Him, "Are you the one who was to come, or should we expect someone else?"

Jesus answered, "Go back and report to John what you hear and see: The blind receive sight, the lame walk, those who have leprosy are cured, the deaf hear, the dead are raised, and the good news is preached to the poor."

The men went away to tell John. When John heard what Jesus had said, he knew that his own cousin, Jesus, was the Christ, the Son of God, about whom he had been preaching.

 SS3809

CRAFT

To complete this bookmark, you will need:

- Crayons or colored pencils
- Scissors
- Hole punch
- Yarn

1. Color the bookmark lightly.
2. Cut out on bold lines.
3. Fold on dotted line.
4. Punch holes where indicated.
5. Lace yarn through holes to form an attractive edging.

Fold

Jesus said, "I am the way and the truth and the life."
        Read John 14:6.

Jesus said, "I am the light of the world."
        Read John 8:12.

Jesus said, "I am the resurrection and the life."
        Read John 11:25.

Jesus said, "I am the good shepherd."
        Read John 10:11.

Do you believe that Jesus is the Christ, the Son of God? Read John 20:31.

TWELVE BASKETS OF FOOD
Based on John 6:4-14

A huge crowd of people had come to listen to Jesus. There were five thousand men, some of whom had brought wives and children. He knew they were hungry. He needed food Himself. But they had come to hear Him teach, and He didn't want them to have to leave in search of food.

Jesus asked His disciple Philip, "Where shall we buy bread for these people to eat?"

Philip said, "Eight months' wages would not buy enough bread for each one to have a bite!"

Even at that high cost, there was no food for sale because the Passover Feast was coming.

Andrew said, "Here is a boy with five small barley loaves and two small fish, but how far will they go among so many?"

Jesus looked at the small lunch. "Have the people sit down," He said. There was plenty of grass in that place and the people all sat down in groups. Jesus gave thanks for the food. Then He passed the bread and fish among them, from group to group.

They all ate and were full. Everyone felt better. "Gather up the pieces that are leftover. Let nothing be wasted," Jesus told His disciples. They found some large baskets —twelve of them—and put the food that was left in them.

Thousands of people had eaten, and twelve baskets were filled with leftovers from those five small loaves and two little fish! After the multitude saw this miracle, they began to say, "Surely this is the Prophet who is to come into the world."

   SS3809

CRAFT

To complete a fish and bread basket, you will need:

- Crayons
- Scissors
- Small, paper lunch bag

1. Color the fish and loaves of bread.
2. Cut them out.
3. Place two fish and five loaves in a lunch bag.

A WALK ON THE LAKE

Based on Matthew 14:22-33

Jesus was preaching and teaching on the shore of a large lake. He planned to do the same on the other side of the lake the next day.

Before Jesus sent the crowd away, He told His disciples to take the boat and go on ahead of Him to the other side. After the people left, He went up on a mountain to pray.

That evening there was a strong wind blowing from the other side of the lake, and it was slow rowing for the disciples. The darkness came, and in the middle of the night the disciples were still rowing. Waves were breaking over the bow of the boat. Jesus went to them walking on the water. One of the men cried out, "It's a ghost." They were terrified.

Jesus said, "Take courage! It is I. Don't be afraid."

"Lord, if it's You, tell me to come to You on the water," called Peter.

"Come," was the answer. Peter got out of the boat and walked on the water toward Jesus. As he came nearer to the Lord, he began to notice the wind beating on him, and he was suddenly afraid. The wind had become a real storm. Peter started to sink. He was very worried. "Lord, save me," he called out.

Reaching out His hand, Jesus caught Peter and said, "You of little faith, why did you doubt?"

Together they walked on the water to the boat. When they got into the boat the wind stopped blowing. The sea became calm. The disciples in the boat who had been so worried fell down and worshiped Jesus. "Truly You are the Son of God," they all agreed.

SS3809

CRAFT

To complete this corner bookmark, you will need:

- Crayons or colored pencils
- Scissors
- Glue

1. Color the bookmark lightly with crayons or colored pencils.

2. Cut it out.

3. Fold on dotted lines.

4. Apply glue on tab.

5. Fasten to form a cone shape and let dry.

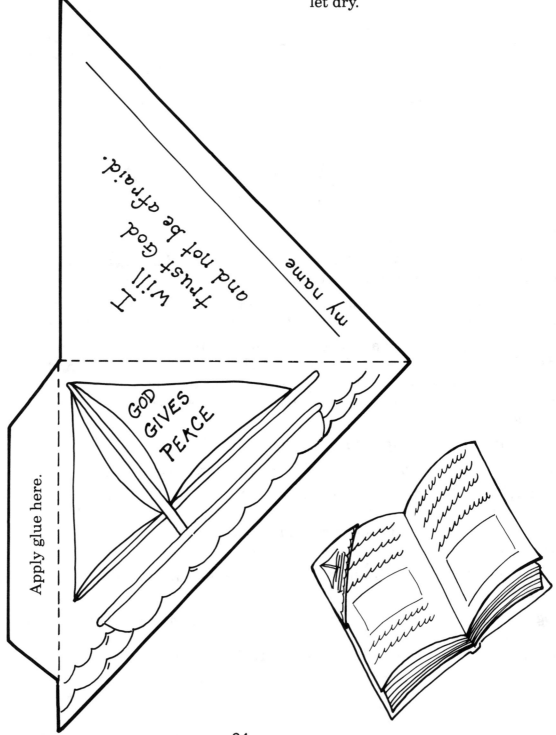

Will I
trust God
and not be afraid.

my name

GOD GIVES PEACE

Apply glue here.

SS3809

GOOD SOIL
Based on Matthew 13:1-23

One day Jesus was talking to a huge crowd of people who had come to hear His teachings. He told them this story.

"A farmer went out to sow his seed. As he was scattering the seed, some fell along the path, and the birds came and ate it up. Some fell on rocky places, where it did not have much soil. It sprang up quickly, because the soil was shallow. But when the sun came up, the plants were scorched, and they withered because they had no roots. Other seed fell among the thorns, which grew up and choked the plants. Still other seed fell on good soil, where it produced a crop—a hundred, sixty, or thirty times what was sown."

Then Jesus called out, "He who has ears, let him hear." His disciples didn't understand and asked Him what He had meant.

Jesus told them, "The knowledge of the secrets of the kingdom of heaven have been given to you, but not to them. I speak to them in parables. Though seeing, they do not see; though hearing, they do not hear or understand."

This is the meaning of His story: The seed is the Word of God. Some people hear it, but the devil comes and snatches it away from their hearts so they will not believe and be saved. The seed sown along the path represents them.

The seed sown among the rocks is like the Word that is received by people with joy when they hear it, but they have no root. They believe for a while but in times of testing they fall away.

The seed that fell among the thorns stands for the Word that is heard by people, but as they go on their way they are choked by life's worries, riches, and pleasures, so that they do not mature.

The seed sown on the good soil stands for the Word that is received by people who believe it and go on to live productive lives for God.

SS3809

CRAFT

To complete this memory verse growth chart, you will need:

- Crayons
- Scissors

1. Color the pattern.

2. Cut it out on the bold lines including the two curved lines.

3. Accordion fold it on the broken lines as shown.

4. Fasten the folded area under the curved flaps to hold.

5. Memorize the first two Bible verses; then fold the next area and watch the plant "grow" as you learn about the Lord.

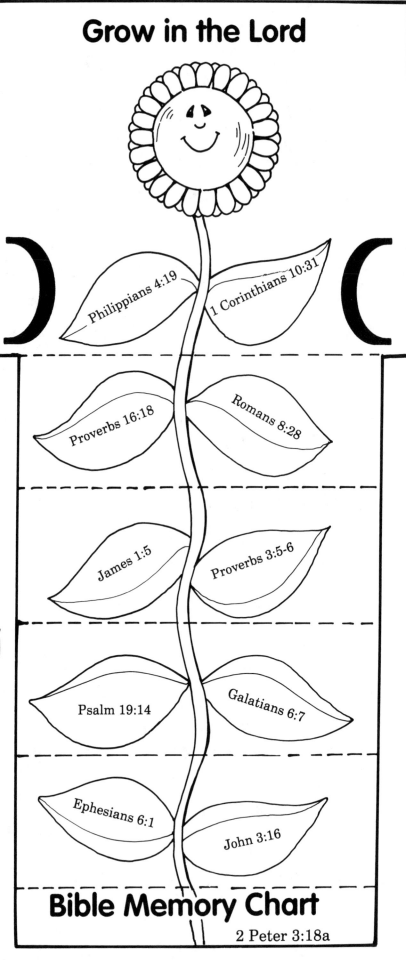

Grow in the Lord

Philippians 4:19

1 Corinthians 10:31

Proverbs 16:18

Romans 8:28

James 1:5

Proverbs 3:5-6

Psalm 19:14

Galatians 6:7

Ephesians 6:1

John 3:16

Bible Memory Chart

2 Peter 3:18a

SS3809

GOD CARES FOR SPARROWS
Matthew 10:26-31

Jesus was giving final instructions to His disciples before sending them out to preach and teach and heal in His name. Some of them were a little frightened. They wondered how people would accept them. Would they listen to the message the disciples had to share? Would some people get angry and try to hurt them? Jesus had some enemies. Would they turn people against the disciples?

Jesus understood their concerns. He had told His disciples, "I am sending you out like sheep among wolves!" He knew they would need courage to face the hardships and dangers they would meet. He said to them, "Do not be afraid of those who kill the body but cannot kill the soul."

He pointed to some sparrows and explained that God watched over them, the most common bird around. If God cared that much for sparrows, how much more He would care for those doing His work. "Even the very hairs of your head are all numbered," Jesus told them. They did not have to be afraid for God would take care of them.

Shining Star Publications, Copyright © 1994 SS3809

CRAFT

To complete this bird-feeding picture, you will need:

- Crayons

- Scissors

- Brad fastener

1. Color the bird and the feeding tray.

2. Cut out on bold lines.

3. Insert brad fastener through black dot in the bird and then through the black dot in picture.

4. Move the bird up and down to look like it is eating birdseed.

* If desired, glue real birdseed on tray.

SS3809

THE WOMAN AND THE PERFUME
Based on Luke 7:36-50

Jesus was invited for dinner to the home of a Pharisee named Simon. As Jesus was eating, a woman entered the room. She was carrying an expensive jar of perfume. She began weeping in sorrow. The woman wet Jesus' feet with her tears, wiped them with her hair, kissed them, and then poured perfume on them. The room was filled with the scent of the perfume.

Simon thought to himself that this was a sinful woman. He wondered why Jesus was allowing her to touch Him.

"Simon, I have something to tell you," said Jesus.

"Tell me teacher," answered Simon.

"Two men owed money to a moneylender," Jesus said. "One owed him five hundred *denarii, and the other fifty. Neither of them had the money to pay him back, so he canceled the debts of both. Now which of them will love him more?"

"I suppose the one who had the bigger debt canceled," answered Simon.

"You have judged correctly," said Jesus.

Then Jesus turned toward the woman and said to Simon, "Do you see this woman? I came into your house. You did not give Me any water for My feet, but she wet My feet with her tears and wiped them with her hair. You did not give Me a kiss, but this woman, from the time I entered, has not stopped kissing My feet. You did not put oil on My head, but she has poured perfume on My feet. Therefore, I tell you, her many sins have been forgiven–for she loved much. But he who has been forgiven little loves little."

Jesus said to the woman, "Your sins are forgiven."

The other guests began to ask among themselves, "Who is this who even forgives sins?"

Jesus said to the woman, "Your faith has saved you; go in peace."

* One denarius was equal to about a day's wages.

SS3809

CRAFT

To complete the room freshener, you will need:

- Crayons
- Scissors
- Glue
- Ground cinnamon
- Granulated sugar
- Whole cloves (optional)

1. Color areas A and B red, brown, or yellow.

2. Spread an even layer of glue over areas A and B.

3. Immediately sprinkle a thick layer of cinnamon and sugar (about one tablespoon that is half cinnamon and half sugar).

4. Gently shake off excess cinnamon and sugar; then allow to dry.

5. Cut out the craft.

6. Fold on broken lines and glue together on tab to form a cone shape.

7. If desired, glue whole cloves randomly on the cone or in an attractive pattern to add a pleasant aroma.

8. Set the cone in a room for a spicy room freshener.

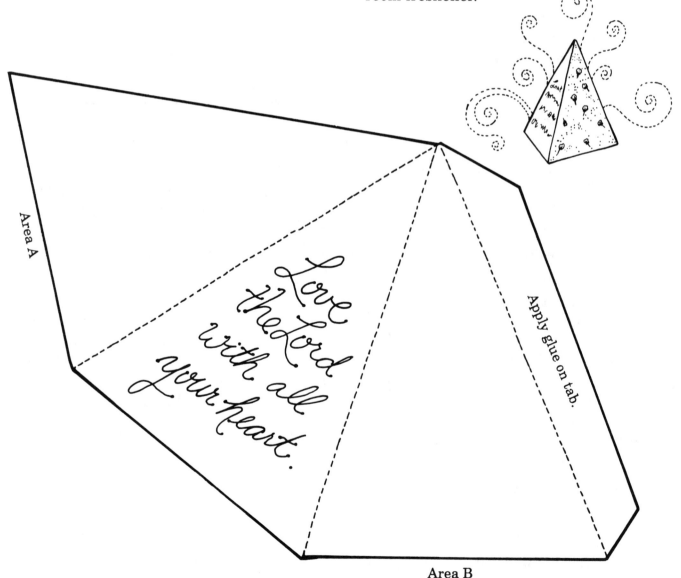

Area A

Love the Lord with all your heart.

Apply glue on tab.

Area B

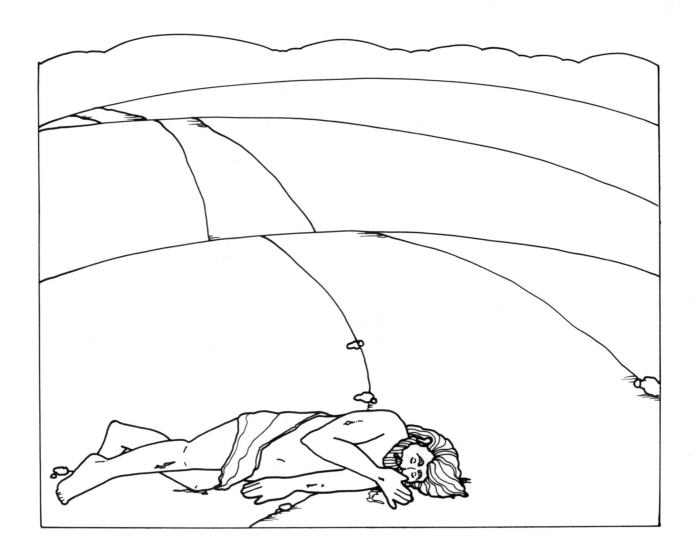

THE GOOD SAMARITAN

Based on Luke 10:25-37

Jesus often told stories to help people understand important truths.

While Jesus was teaching one day, a man asked Him, "What must I do to inherit eternal life?"

Jesus asked, "What is written in the Law?"

The man said, " 'Love the Lord your God with all your heart and with all your soul and with all your strength and with all your mind,' and, 'Love your neighbor as yourself.' "

Jesus replied, "Do this and you will live."

"But who is my neighbor?" asked the man.

Instead of just giving the man an answer, Jesus told this story.

A Jewish man was going from Jerusalem to Jericho when he fell into the hands of some robbers. They stripped him of his clothes, beat him, and went away, leaving him half dead.

SS3809

A Jewish priest came walking along the same road. When he saw the injured man, he crossed to the other side of the road and hurried by.

Next came a Levite, a Jewish religious leader. He also went to the other side of the road and hurried by.

Then along came a Samaritan. Most Samaritans and Jews were considered enemies, but this Samaritan helped the injured man. He poured oil and wine on the man's wounds. He did the best he could to give the man first aid.

Then the Samaritan put the Jewish man on his own donkey, took him to an inn, and took care of him. The next day he took out two silver coins and gave them to the innkeeper. "Take care of this man," he said. "Whatever more it costs, I will pay you when I return."

Then Jesus asked, "Which man acted like a good neighbor?"

The man replied, "The one who showed mercy."

Jesus told the man, "Go and do likewise."

Shining Star Publications, Copyright © 1994 SS3809

CRAFT

To complete this get-well card, you will need:

- Crayons
- Scissors
- 6½" x 3½" envelope
- Postage stamp

1. Color the get-well card.

2. Cut it out on the bold lines.

3. Fold on the broken lines.

4. Print your name and whom you want to send it to on the lines.

5. Use envelope to mail the card.

This card was colored for you by...

Name

God Cares About You

God promised that He would be with you and help you if you ask Him. Trust Him today.

Sending this cheerful greeting
To say "Hello" and then
Hope it won't be very long
Until you're well again.

From _____

SS3809

SERVANTS OF JESUS

Based on Matthew 28:18-20

When Jesus left this earth to go to be with His Father in heaven, He told His followers to tell the whole world the Good News about Him, starting in Jerusalem. He wants us to be His servants, too, telling our friends that God loves them.

Jesus loves us all so much. He proved His love by dying for our sins. He wants people to be in heaven with Him someday. He doesn't want anyone to miss that chance. That's why we need to tell others about Him.

Do you share your love for Jesus and His love for you with other people? Are you a servant of Jesus? Think of all He has done for you. Then think of some ways you can serve Him.

Serving Jesus is the most wonderful way you could ever spend your life!

SS3809

CRAFT

To complete this tract, you will need:

- Crayons
- Scissors

1. Color and cut out the pattern on this page.
2. Fold it in fourths.
3. Give the tract to a friend to share the message of God's love.

*If you wish to make more than one tract, reproduce two copies and cut out. Then lay side by side on a standard 8½" x 11" paper and copy. May copy on light-colored paper if you do not want to color each picture.

How to ask Jesus to be your Savior and Friend

♥ Admit you do wrong.

"For all have sinned." Romans 3:23a

"Search me, O God, and know my heart." Psalm 139:23a

♥ Believe that Jesus died for you by shedding His blood on the cross as He took the punishment for your sin.

"Christ died for us." Romans 5:8b

♥ Pray to God. Tell Him you are sorry for your sin and that you believe in Jesus as the only way to get rid of your sin.

"We believe that Jesus died and rose again." 1 Thessalonians 4:14a

---

GOD LOVES YOU

God wants to be your friend. He wants you to live forever with Him in heaven.

God loves you very much but He hates the bad things you do. He said sin must be punished.

He sent His Son, Jesus Christ, to earth to take the punishment for your sin. Jesus died on a cross so that by believing in Him you can have your sins forgiven.

The gift of God is eternal life. Read Romans 6:23.

Learn more about God's love by reading His book, the Bible.

"God is Love." 1 John 4:16b

"Trust in the Lord and do good." Psalm 37:3a

The Lord is my helper Read Hebrews 13:6.

You can talk to God anytime by praying.

"GOD SAID, '. . . call upon me, and I will answer him; I will be with him in trouble, I will deliver him and honor him.'" Psalm 91:15

GOD IS LOVE.
Read 1 John 4:16.

Somebody Loves You

THE WIDOW AND THE JUDGE

Based on Luke 18:1-7

Jesus told this story to teach His disciples the importance of praying and never giving up.

In a certain town there was a judge who did not fear God or care about people.

A widow in that town, who had been mistreated, went to the judge for help. "Don't bother me now. Go away!" he told her.

Although the judge put her off many times, the widow kept coming back. "Please, your honor, help me," she begged. But he ignored her every time.

She continued to see the judge, asking the same thing every time, "Please help me." She was becoming a problem, always there, always asking for help. Finally the judge gave in. He said to himself, "Even though I have no respect for God or people I will help this woman. If I don't, she will wear me out with her continual pleading."

He finally helped the woman because she asked so often.

Jesus told His disciples that they should never stop praying and talking to God. He asked, "Will not God bring about justice for His chosen ones, who cry out to Him day and night? Will He keep putting them off? I tell you, He will see that they get justice, and quickly."

SS3809

CRAFT

To complete this cloud picture, you will need:

- Crayons
- Glue
- Scissors
- Cotton balls

1. Color the picture of Jesus below.
2. Cut out.
3. Fold on dotted line.

4. Apply glue to the outside top of the folded area.
5. Apply fluffed-up cotton balls on the glued area to resemble a cloud.

Open and close the picture as a reminder that Jesus is listening in heaven when we pray.

SS3809

THE ACCEPTABLE PRAYER

Based on Luke 18:9-14

Jesus told this story to teach His followers how to pray.

Two men went into the temple to pray. One was a Pharisee, a leader in the synagogue; the other was a tax collector. In those days, some tax collectors were unpopular because they cheated people.

The leader of the synagogue stood right in the middle of the temple and looked over at the tax collector. He laughed to himself. Then he lifted his arms and prayed, "Lord, I thank You that I am not like other men, like that tax collector over there. I fast twice a week and give a tithe for everything I get." The Pharisee felt he was worthy of God's love.

The tax collector stood quietly in a corner of the temple. He was so ashamed, he lowered his head and didn't even lift his eyes to heaven. "God, have mercy on me, a sinner," he prayed.

Jesus told His disciples that the tax collector's prayer was more acceptable to God. "For everyone who exalts himself will be humbled," He said, "and he who humbles himself will be exalted."

CRAFT

To complete this stand-up plaque, you will need:

- Crayons
- Scissors

1. Color the pattern below.

2. Cut it out.

3. Fold on the broken line.

4. Stand the plaque in your room where it will remind you why you should be humble when you pray.

Worship God Only
"Praise the Lord, for the Lord is good."
Psalm 135:3a

God is holy and just. He hates wrong,
but rewards those who love and trust Him.

SS3809

THE TRIUMPHAL ENTRY

Based on Mark 10:32-34; 11:1-10

One day Jesus took His disciples aside and told them what was going to happen to Him. "We are going up to Jerusalem," He said, "and the Son of Man will be betrayed to the chief priests and teachers of the law. They will condemn Him to death and will hand Him over to the Gentiles, who will mock Him and spit on Him, flog Him and kill Him. Three days later He will rise."

When He and His disciples came nearer to Jerusalem, He called two of them aside. He told them to go ahead into the city, where they would find the colt of a donkey on which no one had ridden. They were to untie the colt and bring it to Him. If anyone asked what they were doing, they were to say that the Lord needed the colt. The disciples did what Jesus had told them and brought the animal to Him.

As Jesus entered Jerusalem riding on the donkey colt, the people greeted Him with shouts of joy. They spread their coats and palm branches on the road for Him to ride over. He came into town as a servant. The people welcomed Him as they would welcome royalty! "Hosanna!" they shouted. "Blessed is He who comes in the name of the Lord!"

CRAFT

To complete this Easter card, you will need:

- Crayons
- Scissors
- Standard business-sized envelope
- Postage stamp

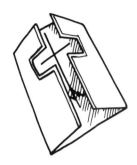

1. Color and cut out the card.
2. Fold on the dotted lines.
3. Color the front of the card using a light spring color.
4. Sign the card, place it in an envelope, and mail it to a friend or relative.

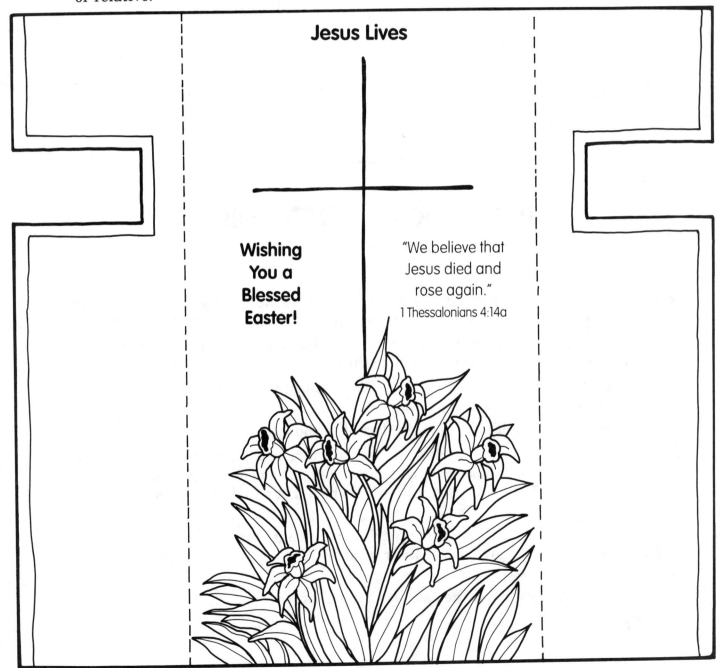

Jesus Lives

Wishing You a Blessed Easter!

"We believe that Jesus died and rose again."
1 Thessalonians 4:14a

SS3809

THE WIDOW'S OFFERING

Based on Mark 12:41-44

Jesus sat in the temple, watching people put money into the offering for the work of the Lord. As He watched, quite a few well-dressed men put money into the offering box.

Each man threw a large amount of money in the box, and the bystanders were impressed. The sound of coins dropping into the offering box was loud in the temple.

Then a poor widow came into the temple. She dropped two small copper coins—worth less than a penny—into the offering box.

Jesus called to His disciples, "Come here. I want to show you something."

The disciples gathered around Him. He asked them to look at the poorly dressed widow. He told them he had been watching rich men put lots of money into the offering box for God's work. Then this poor widow had come along and put in just two copper coins.

Jesus said, "I tell you the truth, this poor widow has put more into the treasury than all the others. They all gave out of their wealth; but she, out of her poverty, put in everything—all she had to live on."

It was an important lesson for the disciples and for us.

SS3809

CRAFT

To complete this billfold, you will need:

- Crayons
- Scissors

1. Color and cut out the billfold.

2. Fold it as shown.

3. Start saving your money, keeping it in this billfold to give to the Lord.

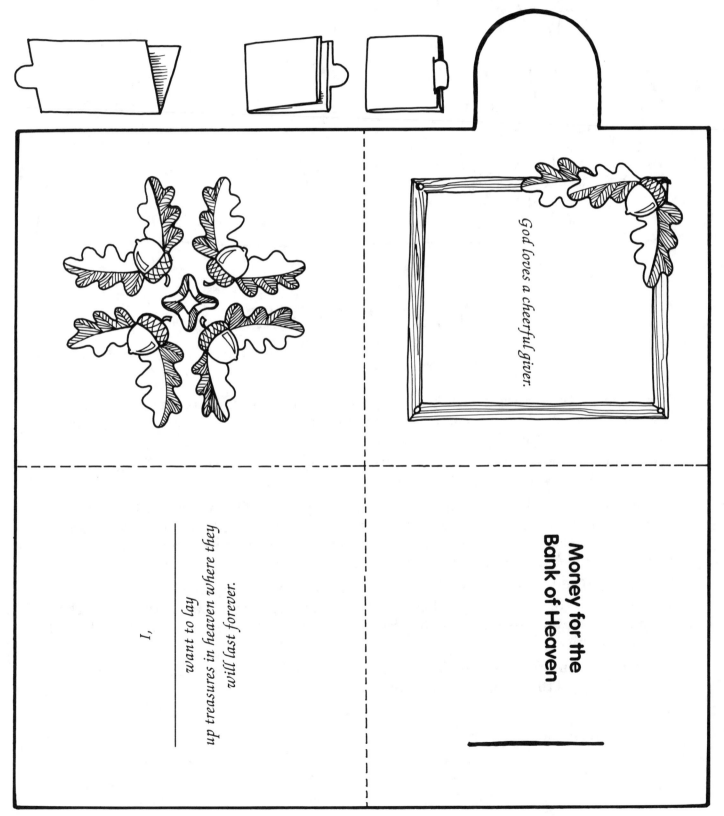

God loves a cheerful giver.

Money for the
Bank of Heaven

I,

want to lay
up treasures in heaven where they
will last forever.

SS3809

AN EMPTY TOMB

Based on Matthew 28:1-8

It was very early on the morning of the third day after Jesus was crucified. It was a beautiful morning; the sun was just coming up. However, two women walking quickly toward Jesus' tomb hardly noticed the sunshine.

They had left very early and walked all the way from the village. "There's the garden," said one. "We're getting close." They walked a little faster.

When they got to the tomb, the women had a surprise. The big stone, blocking the entrance to the tomb, was rolled away! They walked up to the tomb and saw an angel sitting on the tombstone. He was wearing a spotless, sparkling white robe. The soldiers who were supposed to be guarding the tomb had run away.

"Do not be afraid," the angel said to the women, "I know you are looking for Jesus, who was crucified. He is not here; He has risen! Come and see the place where He lay. Then go quickly and tell His disciples that He is going ahead of them into Galilee. He will see them there."

Jesus had been dead, but God had given Him new life! Filled with joy, the women rushed off to tell the disciples that Jesus was alive!

SS3809

CRAFT

To complete this resurrection picture, you will need:

- Crayons
- Scissors
- Brad fastener

1. Color the "stone" and the picture below.

2. Cut them both out.

3. Attach the stone to the entrance of the tomb, using a brad fastener poked through the two black dots. The stone may be rolled away from the tomb, then closed again.

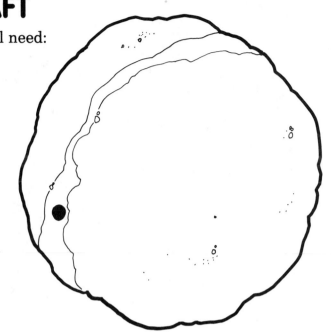

JESUS LIVES

JESUS COMES TO SEE HIS FRIENDS

Based on Luke 24:36-53

The disciples were eating dinner, discussing reports they had heard of Jesus' empty tomb. They were puzzled.

Suddenly Jesus entered the room. He didn't bother with the door; He just walked through the wall! The disciples were so surprised, some of them thought they were seeing a ghost!

"Peace be with you," He said. "Why are you troubled, and why do doubts rise in your minds? Look at My hands and My feet. It is I myself! Touch Me and see; a ghost does not have flesh and bones, as you see I have."

The disciples gasped in astonishment. Jesus asked them, "Do you have anything here to eat?" They gave Him a piece of broiled fish, and He ate it right there among them. They were amazed. This *really was* Jesus, in the flesh, alive!

"This is what I told you while I was still with you," He said. "Everything must be fulfilled that is written about Me in the Law of Moses, the Prophets, and the Psalms. The Christ will suffer and rise from the dead on the third day, and repentance and forgiveness of sins will be preached in His name to all nations. You are witnesses of these things."

Later Jesus met His disciples in Bethany where He blessed them; then He was carried up into heaven. The disciples worshiped Him and were filled with joy.

SS3809

CRAFT

To make name cards for your dinner table, you will need:

- Crayons
- Scissors
- Pencil
- Tracing or lightweight paper

1. Trace the name card below for each member of your family.
2. Color the cards.
3. Cut them out on the bold lines around the edge and around the top of the cross.
4. Fold on the broken line, allowing the cross to pop up.
5. Print each person's name on the line.
6. Put a card next to each person's place at the table.

A MIGHTY WIND
Based on Acts 2:1-41

After Jesus went back to heaven, His disciples stayed in Jerusalem. One day they were all together in a house when a wonderful thing happened. Suddenly the air was filled with a sound like a mighty, rushing wind! Then they saw what looked like small flames of fire on each other. These were signs from God that He was giving them His Holy Spirit.

There were godly Jews from other nations in Jerusalem that day. They had come to celebrate Pentecost. Many of them heard the sound and came running. The disciples spoke to them, and each foreigner heard the disciples speaking in his own language! All were amazed. "Are not all these men who are speaking Galileans?" they asked. "How is it that each of us hears them in our own native language?" Amazed and puzzled, they asked each other, "What does this mean?"

Peter, standing with the other disciples, spoke to the crowd: "All of you who live in Jerusalem, let me explain this to you; listen carefully to what I say. Jesus of Nazareth was a man accredited by God to you by miracles, wonders and signs, which God did among you through Him, as you yourselves know. This man was handed over to you by God's set purpose and foreknowledge; and you, with the help of wicked men, put Him to death by nailing Him to the cross. But God raised Him from the dead. God made this Jesus, whom you crucified, both Lord and Christ."

The people were very sad to hear this and asked Peter what they should do. Peter told them to repent and be baptized. Three thousand people became believers that day!

CRAFT

To complete this wall plaque, you will need:

- Crayons
- Scissors
- Glue
- Two craft sticks
- String

1. Color the pattern on this page.
2. Cut it out.
3. Fold tabs under and glue a craft stick under each tab as shown.
4. Tie a 6" length of string on both sides of the top craft stick to form a hanger.

Tab

Repent and be baptized, every one of you, in the name of Jesus Christ. Read Acts 2:38.

Tab

89

SS3809

SAUL MEETS JESUS
Based on Acts 9:1-31

Saul of Tarsus was walking one day on the road to Damascus. He was planning mistreatment for the believers there. He had brought great trouble to those in Jerusalem who believed in Jesus. Now he was planning to find and arrest people in Damascus who worshiped Jesus.

Suddenly a bright light stopped him in his tracks. He was blinded and fell to the ground. He heard a voice say, "Saul, Saul, why do you persecute Me?"

"Who are you, Lord?" Saul asked.

"I am Jesus, whom you are persecuting," said the voice. "Now get up and go into the city, and you will be told what you must do." The men with Saul were very frightened. They had heard the voice but had not seen anything.

Saul got up from the ground, but he could not see. The men led him by the hand to the city of Damascus. For three days he was blind, and he didn't eat or drink anything.

Living in Damascus was a man named Ananias, a follower of the Lord. Jesus appeared to him in a vision and told him how to find Saul. Ananias was afraid. He knew Saul persecuted Jesus' followers, but he went anyway. He found Saul and spoke to him about the Lord. He laid his hands on him as Jesus had told him, and Saul regained his sight.

Saul believed right away and was baptized as a follower of Jesus. He spent several days with the Damascus believers he had intended to have arrested. He went to every synagogue he could find, announcing for all to hear that, "Jesus is the Son of God!" Everyone was amazed at the change in him.

Saul later became known as Paul. He preached about Jesus and is still helping people come to know the Lord through the books he wrote in the Bible.

SS3809

CRAFT

To complete the sunglasses, you will need:

- Crayons
- Glue
- Scissors

1. Color the pieces below.
2. Cut them out on outside lines, and cut out the two circles in the frame.
3. Glue the pieces together and fold on dotted lines to form sunglasses.

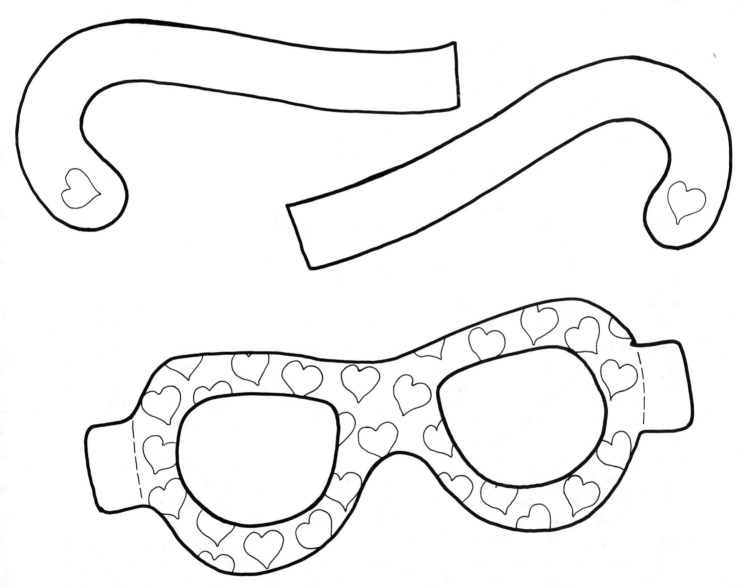

Saul was blinded by the light of Jesus' glory. Would sunglasses have helped?

No, but they'll help you remember what happened to Saul.

PETER AND THE ANGEL
Based on Acts 12:1-17

Herod was a wicked king in Israel. He persecuted Jesus' followers. He killed James, the brother of John. When he saw that this pleased the Jews, he also arrested Peter.

Herod planned to bring Peter out of prison for a public trial at Passover time. The night before he could do that, Peter, bound in chains, was sleeping between two soldiers. An angel of the Lord appeared and a light shone in the cell. The angel struck Peter in the side and woke him. He said, "Quick, get up!" Immediately the chains fell off Peter's hands. Then the angel said, "Put on your clothes and sandals. Wrap your cloak around you and follow me."

Peter followed, even though he thought he was just seeing a vision. They walked right past both guards, then came to an iron gate. The gate opened for them by itself. They left the prison and walked down the street. Then the angel left Peter. That's when he realized that the Lord had sent His angel to rescue him.

He went to the house of Mary, the mother of Mark, where many believers were gathered to pray for him. When he knocked on the gate, a maid came to answer. She didn't open the gate, but ran and told the others that Peter was standing there. "You're out of your mind," they all said to her. "If anything is there it is his ghost."

Peter kept knocking and they finally opened the gate. When they saw that it was really Peter, they were amazed. He told them how the angel had rescued him, and they all praised God.

SS3809

CRAFT

To complete the praying hands wall plaque, you will need:

- Crayons
- Scissors
- Glue
- Two paper plates
- String
- Hole punch (optional)

1. Color the pattern below. Color the inside of one of the paper plates yellow.

2. Enlarge and cut out the pattern on the bold lines including around the hands.

3. Glue it to the back (bottom) side of the other paper plate. Then cut out the area inside the pattern behind the hands again.

4. Glue the paper plates together with the rims facing each other so that yellow can be seen around the hands.

5. Punch holes where indicated.

6. To make a hanger, attach a short length of string through the holes and tie.

"He will call upon me, and I will answer him; I will be with him in trouble, I will deliver him and honor him."

Psalm 91:15

SS3809

SHIPWRECK!
Based on Acts 27:4-28:11

Paul was a prisoner on a ship, sailing to Rome to be tried by Caesar. The ship sailed along nicely until winter winds came up. The crew was afraid. They wanted to get to Crete, where there was a good harbor. They could stay there and be safe for the winter.

The wind began to blow more gently, so they lost their fear and kept sailing along the Island of Crete. Paul argued that they should spend the winter there, but the captain and crew wanted to leave. After they left, the wind came up hard again and blew them towards a small island named Cauda. They tried to prepare the ship for stormy weather. A little later a strong wind came across the land, and they were driven out to sea.

Everybody was afraid. They threw the cargo overboard to lighten the ship, but it was still in danger of sinking. Paul told the crew, "Last night an angel of the God whose I am and whom I serve stood beside me and said, 'Do not be afraid, Paul. You must stand trial before Caesar; and God has graciously given you the lives of all who sail with you.' "

It wasn't long until the ship was blown toward an island. At dawn Paul told the crew that they must eat, for they would need strength. Paul took bread, broke it, and gave thanks to God for the food in front of all those on board. They ate and then threw the rest of the food overboard to try to make the ship lighter and more manageable.

Driven by the wind, the ship moved closer and closer to the rocky beach. Then the ship ran aground on a sandbar. It began to break up and everyone dove into the water. Some drifted ashore on planks, while others swam to safety to the island of Malta.

It started to rain, and the people of the island made fires to warm the shipwrecked visitors. Paul and the crew stayed there for three months. They were well treated by the people of the island and well protected by God.

SS3809

CRAFT

To complete this 3-D framed verse, you will need:

- Crayons
- Scissors
- Glue
- String (optional)

1. Color the pattern below.
2. Cut it out on the bold lines.
3. Slightly fold the four sides forward.
4. Apply glue on the tabs and fasten to make a 3-D picture frame.

* If desired, glue or tape a short length of string to the back for a hanger.

Tab   Tab

"When I am afraid, I
will trust in you."
Psalm 56:3

Tab   Tab

𝔅ible 𝔎nowledge 𝔄ward

to

_____

(name)

for learning God's truths
through Bible stories, and
for applying them to your life.

". . . you will know the
truth, and the truth will
set you free."
John 8:32

SS3809